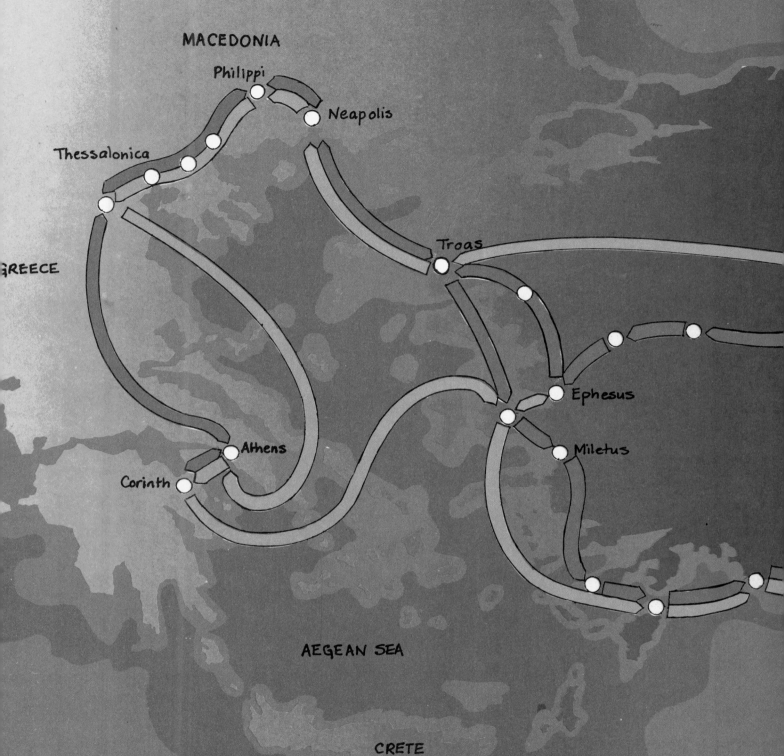

KU-048-876

BLACK SEA

MACEDONIA

Philippi

Neapolis

Thessalonica

GREECE

Troas

Athens

Ephesus

Corinth

Miletus

AEGEAN SEA

CRETE

MEDITERRANEAN SEA

2nd voyage

3rd voyage

Hodder & Stoughton Bible Albums No. 9

PAUL, THE CHURCH-BUILDER

Editorial Committee
Father René Berthier
Jeanne-Marie Faure
Marie-Hélène Sigaut

Illustrated by
Lizzie Napoli

Translated by
Jane Collins

British Library Cataloguing in Publication Data
Berthier, René
   Paul, the church-builder. – (Hodder and Stoughton
   Bible albums; vol. 9).
   1. Paul, *Saint* – Juvenile literature
   I. Title   II. Faure, Jeanne-Marie
   III. Sigaut, Marie-Hélène
   225.9'24   BS2506.5

   ISBN 0-340-25333-9

First published 1980
Original text and illustrations © 1979 by Univers-Media
English translation © 1980 by Hodder and Stoughton Ltd.
All rights reserved. No part of this publication
may be reproduced or transmitted in any form or
by any means, electronic or mechanical,
including photocopying, recording, or any
information storage and retrieval system,
without permission in writing from the publisher.

Printed in Belgium for Hodder and Stoughton Ltd.,
Mill Road, Dunton Green, Sevenoaks, Kent by
Henri Proost & Cie, Turnhout.

The text at the end of this volume is reproduced from the
New International Version of the Bible © 1978 by
New York International Bible Society,
published by Hodder & Stoughton.

HODDER AND STOUGHTON
LONDON   SYDNEY   AUCKLAND   TORONTO

BY THE YEAR 50 A.D., PAUL HAS ALREADY SPREAD THE GOSPEL THROUGHOUT ASIA MINOR. LED BY THE HOLY SPIRIT, HE NOW EXPANDS HIS HORIZONS AND MOVES EASTWARDS. HE SAILS TO MACEDONIA, DISEMBARKING AT NEAPOLIS, AND MAKES HIS WAY TOWARDS PHILIPPI FOLLOWING THE VIA EGNATIA, ONE OF THE GREAT ROMAN ROADS.

THE PHILIPPIANS ARE MOSTLY OF ROMAN EXTRACTION, AND THERE ARE AS MANY PEOPLE IN THE TOWN WHO SPEAK LATIN AS SPEAK GREEK.

THE FOLLOWING SABBATH, PAUL AND HIS FRIENDS GO TO THE JEWS' PLACE OF PRAYER.

I have a large house. Please consider it yours to use as you want.

Thank you, but I prefer to owe no-one anything. I earn my living.

I insist. If you believe I am faithful to the Lord, come and live with me.

PAUL FINALLY AGREES, AND MOVES IN WITH TIMOTHY, SILVANUS AND LUKE. MANY PHILIPPIANS COME THERE TO HEAR HIS TEACHING.

ONE DAY, ON THEIR WAY TO A PRAYER MEETING, A WOMAN CRIES OUT:

These men are servants of the Most High God. They can tell you the way to be saved.

If I pay you, will they sort out my problems?

What a nuisance that woman is! The Word of God has nothing to do with her fortune-telling.

I agree, but she earns a lot of money for her owners by predicting such things.

6

THIS SLAVE GIRL FOLLOWS PAUL FOR SEVERAL DAYS, SHOUTING ALL THE TIME. EVENTUALLY PAUL, EXASPERATED, ORDERS HER TO STOP, AND IMMEDIATELY SHE LOSES HER POWER TO TELL FORTUNES. HER OWNERS ARE FURIOUS.

THEY ARREST PAUL AND SILVANUS AND DRAG THEM INTO THE COURTS.

PAUL AND SILVANUS ARE FOUND GUILTY BY THE ROMAN JUDGES OF THE TOWN. THEY ARE WHIPPED AND THEN THROWN INTO PRISON.

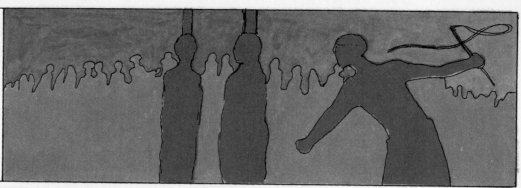

How good you are, Lord, to have planted a Community of believers here at Philippi. May our sufferings inspire them.

Help them to be more loving and understanding, pure as Jesus was and filled with your Spirit.

SUDDENLY, ABOUT MIDNIGHT, THERE IS A GREAT EARTHQUAKE.

Free!

We're free!

ROMAN CITIZENS HAD CERTAIN RIGHTS WHICH HAD TO BE RESPECTED, SO THE ROMAN JUDGES COME TO MAKE PEACE WITH PAUL AND SILVANUS.

Please forgive us. If we had only known more about you, we would have been less hasty in our actions.

Now, to avoid any further trouble, we would be grateful if you left the town.

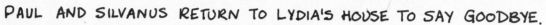

PAUL AND SILVANUS RETURN TO LYDIA'S HOUSE TO SAY GOODBYE.

Luke will stay here with you. But you are all still young in the faith: stay together and stand firm.

Lead a life worthy of the gospel, united in both heart and spirit.

When will you come back?

I don't want to leave; remember I love you all with the love of Jesus himself.

"My heart is glad and my tongue rejoices, because you will not abandon me to the grave, nor let your Holy One see decay. You have made known to me the paths of life."

This psalm was written long before Jesus' time, but as you can see, it speaks of him.

Yes, Jesus was stronger even than death! He was the first to be raised into full life with God, and he invites all who follow him to join him there.

The ideas you proclaim really move me. I am almost prepared to believe you.

You, Jason, leader of the Synagogue? Are you so stupid?

PAUL'S WORDS CONVINCE SOME JEWS AND MANY GREEKS, AND THEY BECOME CHRISTIANS. OTHER JEWS, HOWEVER, STIR UP A RIOT IN THE TOWN. JASON, LEADER OF THE SYNAGOGUE, IS DRAGGED BEFORE THE CITY OFFICIALS.

What will become of them? In these three weeks they haven't had enough time to get to know and love Jesus...

When enemies attack them, will they be able to stand firm? Will Jews and Greeks get on together? Do they have enough love for each other? Who will lead them?

Lord, it is you who called them. They received your Word with joy. You are faithful: keep them in your peace.

SO PAUL ARRIVES IN ATHENS

MEN EVERYWHERE ARE DISCUSSING WHAT LIFE IS ABOUT, AND PAUL JOINS IN WITH THEM.

I've left my house in the charge of a faithful slave: my mind is at peace.

That way you can enjoy the pleasures of poetry and find happiness in life.

You seem very sure of yourself. What is this new teaching?

Our teacher Epicurus would have approved of your wisdom in putting aside daily worries.

You believe that? There's a much deeper joy to be found. Jesus, God's Chosen One, offers it to us.

This fever is wearing me down! My legs won't carry me any further.

I've hardly got enough to spend the night in an inn.

Come on, keep going!

What a lively town! I'm as much a stranger here as in Athens. Still, I should find some work easily.

I see you make tents. That's my line as well. My name is Paul, and I'm a Jew from Tarsus in Cilicia.

Welcome to Corinth! We're also Jews. I'm called Aquila.

This is my wife, Priscilla. We've just come from Rome, because the Emperor Claudius ordered all Jews to leave.

You don't look very well. Why don't you come and lie down?

Thank you. You are real friends. I'll return your kindness by working.

PAUL MOVES IN WITH THEM AND WORKS WITH THEM.

What do you make of the people of Corinth, Paul?

They seem a rough bunch; I'm almost afraid of them, but I must speak to them. The Spirit assures me that many will believe.

SOME TIME LATER SILVANUS AND TIMOTHY ARRIVE FROM THESSALONICA.

After you left Thessalonica, our enemies attacked with renewed vigour. The brothers had to suffer insults, whipping, prison – all kinds of persecution.

And they held firm. Their sufferings only strengthened their faith and in love they supported and comforted one another.

What an encouragement! We haven't worked in vain! How can I thank God enough for this great joy!

THEN SILVANUS AND TIMOTHY QUESTION PAUL ON THE SUBJECT WHICH IS WORRYING THE BROTHERS IN THESSALONICA: IS THE END OF THE WORLD COMING SOON? SO IN THE WINTER OF 50 AD, PAUL DICTATES HIS FIRST TWO LETTERS TO THEM.

You are like my beloved children to me. I remember you constantly with love. Persevere in the way you began; God's will is that you should be holy. Don't worry about the end of the world; no-one knows when it will be. However it comes about, we will be with the Lord for ever. Rejoice always, pray constantly, do not hinder the Spirit of God. The grace of Christ be with you all!

21

22

25

PAUL HAS BEEN AT CORINTH FOR EIGHTEEN MONTHS WHEN HIS JEWISH ENEMIES BEGIN TO STIR UP TROUBLE AGAIN. THEY BRING HIM TO TRIAL BEFORE GALLIO, THE PROCONSUL, WHO WILL NOT HAVE ANYTHING TO DO WITH THE MATTER AND SENDS THEM AWAY. SOME TIME LATER...

Are you leaving?

Yes, we're going to Ephesus to do some business.

I'm going with them. I must make contact again with Jerusalem, Antioch and the Communities in Asia Minor.

I can see that the church of Corinth must be united with all the others, but we'll miss you.

The Corinthians are full of new life, but have many faults.

It will be difficult to lead them without you.

I know. They are still children in many ways, but I must try to trust them. As elders, you will be able to look after them.

PAUL SETS SAIL WITH HIS FRIENDS PRISCILLA AND AQUILA, WHO DISEMBARK AT EPHESUS. HE GOES ON ALONE TO CAESAREA, AND FROM THERE HE TRAVELS TO JERUSALEM, THEN ANTIOCH.

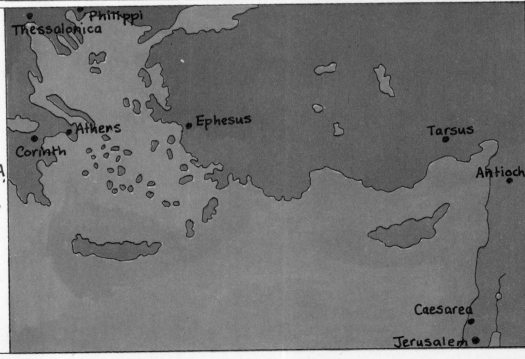

Philippi
Thessalonica
Athens
Corinth
Ephesus
Tarsus
Antioch
Caesarea
Jerusalem

I am full of admiration for your faith, Apollos, and your gift for speaking about Jesus Christ.

We are his disciples as well.

I'm lucky enough to have been able to study a lot. It's very useful for convincing the Jews.

Which you do very well. But you don't seem to know the whole gospel.

Would you allow us to talk to you as a brother, and to teach you what else we know?

I'd love to hear what you have to say, though I'm leaving for Greece in a few days.

Actually, we've just come from Corinth. There's a large church there. I'll write a letter to those brothers so they can receive you properly.

WHILE APOLLOS IS IN CORINTH, PAUL ARRIVES AT EPHESUS WITH HIS COMPANIONS.

How good to see you in one piece after that long journey.

You look very strained, and you've lost weight too!

We've walked hundreds of miles on the roads of Asia Minor. We've been hungry, thirsty, cold, not had enough sleep...

We've known danger too: danger from rivers, danger from bandits, danger in the city, danger in the country, danger from false brothers.

And then I am constantly worried about all the churches...

What you need is to stay here a while and rest.

We can't. The love of Christ drives us on. Woe to me if I don't preach the gospel!

PAUL STAYS AT EPHESUS FOR NEARLY THREE YEARS, FROM 54 to 57 A.D. ALL THE TIME APOLLOS IS TEACHING IN CORINTH, THEN HE LEAVES. THE APOSTLE PETER HIMSELF GOES TO VISIT THE CHRISTIANS OF CORINTH.

He was an amazing man to follow. He accepted everybody who came to him in faith. I shall never forget his eyes...

Peter, you spent three years as Jesus' friend. Tell us about him.

It's marvellous to hear you talking about a man of flesh and blood. Tell us more...

ROUND ABOUT EASTER 57 A.D., SOME MESSENGERS BROUGHT NEWS FROM CORINTH TO PAUL.

Paul, the elders of the church of Corinth have sent us to tell you things are not going well. There is no order in the community. We need your help.

Some of the Christians are not living according to the gospel at all. One man has even gone as far as taking his father's wife.

When they come together, it is as if it were not the Lord's meal at all. As soon as they sit down at table, everyone eats what they brought with them, so one man is hungry, while the next gets drunk.

A number of hotheads, under the pretext that they have a special gift from the Holy Spirit, disrupt the meetings and annoy everyone with empty talk.

Brothers have disputes among themselves, and even take each other to court. It's disgraceful!

Then there are others who cause divisions in the church. Some say they follow Peter, some Apollos, some Paul... as if all three groups were not following the same Christ.

This news reduces me to tears. If someone is weak, I feel weak with them. If someone falls, I am shaken to the core.

PAUL WONDERS WHETHER
HE SHOULD GO TO CORINTH.
HERE IN EPHESUS
THE YOUNG COMMUNITY
NEEDS HIM TOO. IN THE
END, HE DECIDES TO
WRITE A LETTER TO
THE CHRISTIANS IN CORINTH:

Paul, apostle of Jesus Christ
by the will of God,
to the community
of believers at Corinth
and also to all men everywhere
who place their hope in Jesus Christ;
grace and peace to you
from God the Father.

PAUL ADMONISHES THEM FOR
THEIR BAD BEHAVIOUR, ASKS
THEM TO RETURN TO ORDER
AND REMEMBER WHAT THEIR FAITH
REQUIRES OF THEM. THEN HE ADDS:

I could speak in every language of men or angels,
be a genius, a fount of knowledge;
but if I have no love,
I am nothing. I could have faith
to move mountains,
surrender my body to the flames,
but if I have no love,
I am good for nothing. Love is patient;
love seeks to serve,
it does not envy,
it does not boast.
It is not selfish,
and keeps no record of wrongs.
Love forgives all things,
believes all things,
hopes all things,
endures all things.
Love will never come to an end.

PAUL HIMSELF BEGINS ANOTHER LETTER.

You foolish Galatians!
Who has bewitched you?
You are sons of God, not slaves!
You are heirs of his riches.
His Spirit is in your hearts,
So that you call God, "Father."
All of you, Jews and Greeks,
slaves and citizens,
men and women,
you are all children of God.
So you are all free.
Free to build each other up, free to love.
The only law is this,
"Bear one another's burdens in love."

THE CROWD RUSHES ALONG TO THE COURTS, WHERE A ROMAN OFFICIAL MANAGES TO CALM THEM:

Citizens, calm down, please! You make too much of this. Everyone knows that Ephesus is the sacred home of Artemis.

This demonstration can only bring you trouble. If Demetrius and his friends wish to settle the matter, they can lodge a complaint in the courts.

BECAUSE OF THIS INCIDENT PAUL LEAVES EARLIER.

After three years with you, you will always be close to me.

Live together in love. Be strong, fair, true and good. Peace be with you. Good-bye!

HE RETURNS VIA PHILIPPI AND THESSALONICA, CHURCHES DEAR TO HIM, AND THEN MOVES TO CORINTH

Your letters were harsh, but they put an end to our problems.

You will find a healthier church now.

This is a great relief to me. You are my pride and joy!

PAUL SPENDS THE WINTER OF 57-58 A.D. AT CORINTH. WHILE THERE, HE WRITES A LETTER TO THE CHRISTIANS IN ROME, FOR IT HAS LONG BEEN HIS DREAM TO PREACH IN THE CENTRE OF THE ROMAN EMPIRE. BUT FIRST, ANOTHER TASK AWAITS:

You know what you told us about the famine in Jerusalem.

We know other Greek churches have sent money to the brothers there, and we want to as well.

Perhaps one day we will need their help...

I knew I could rely on you. Thank you. God loves a generous giver.

You're going to be in charge of a lot of money.

I promise to manage it well. I don't want any criticism on that score.

You know about the generosity of the Lord Jesus Christ: he was rich, but became poor so as to make us rich.

IN MARCH 58 A.D. PAUL SETS OFF FOR JERUSALEM TO TAKE THE GIFT FROM THE GREEK CHURCHES. HE MAKES A SHORT STOP AT TROAS.

I would like to say to you what I wrote to the brothers in Rome: "We may have enemies, we may have problems, but nothing can destroy us, because God is for us. He has given us the most precious gift of all: his Son. This shows that his love has no bounds. Nothing and nobody, I am convinced, can ever tear us from his arms."

41

PAUL ALREADY HAS HIS MIND FIXED ON ROME WHERE HIS FATE AWAITS HIM.

Passages from the New Testament

which have inspired this book

The text is taken from the NEW INTERNATIONAL VERSION of the Bible.

Starting work in Philippi

Acts 16:11-15 page 3

11 From Troas we put out to sea and sailed straight for Samothrace, and the next day on to Neapolis. **12** From there we travelled to Philippi, a Roman colony and the leading city of that district of Macedonia. And we stayed there several days.

13 On the Sabbath we went outside the city gate to the river, where we expected to find a place of prayer. We sat down and began to speak to the women who had gathered there. **14** One of those listening was a woman named Lydia, a dealer in purple cloth from the city of Thyatira, who was a worshipper of God. The Lord opened her heart to respond to Paul's message. **15** When she and the members of her household were baptized, she invited us to her home. "If you consider me a believer in the Lord," she said, "come and stay at my house." And she persuaded us.

Problems arise

Acts 16:16-24 page 6

16 Once when we were going to the place of prayer, we were met by a slave girl who had a spirit by which she predicted the future. She earned a lot of money for her owners by fortune-telling. **17** This girl followed Paul and the rest of us, shouting, "These men are servants of the Most High God, who are telling you the way to be saved." **18** She kept this up for many days. Finally Paul became so troubled that he turned round and said to the spirit, "In the name of Jesus Christ I command you to come out of her!" At that moment the spirit left her.

19 When the owners of the slave girl realized that their hope of making money was gone, they seized Paul and Silas and dragged them into the market-place to face the authorities. **20** They brought them before the magistrates and said, "These men are Jews, and are throwing our city into an uproar **21** by advocating customs unlawful for us Romans to accept or practise."

22 The crowd joined in the attack against Paul and Silas, and the magistrates ordered them to be stripped and beaten. **23** After they had been severely flogged, they were thrown into prison, and the jailer was commanded to guard them carefully. **24** Upon receiving such orders, he put them in the inner cell and fastened their feet in the stocks.

Paul's prayer for the Philippians

Philippians 1:3, 9, 10

3 I thank my God every time I remember you.

9 And this is my prayer: that your love may abound more and more in knowledge and depth of insight, **10** so that you may be able to discern what is best and may be pure and blameless until the day of Christ.

Paul and Silas are released

Acts 16:25-40 page 8

25 About midnight Paul and Silas were praying and singing hymns to God, and the other prisoners were listening to them. **26** Suddenly there was such a violent earthquake that the foundations of the prison were shaken. At once all the prison doors flew open, and everybody's chains came loose. **27** The jailer woke up, and when he saw the prison doors open, he drew his sword and was about to kill himself because he thought the prisoners had escaped. **28** But Paul shouted, "Don't harm yourself! We are all here!"

29 The jailer called for lights, rushed in and fell trembling before Paul and Silas. **30** He then brought them out and asked, "Men, what must I do to be saved?"

31 They replied, "Believe in the Lord Jesus, and you will be saved—you and your household." **32** Then they spoke the word of the Lord to him and to all the others in his house. **33** At that hour of the night the jailer took them and washed their wounds; then immediately he and all his family were baptized. **34** The jailer brought them into his house and set a meal before them, and the whole family was filled with joy, because they had come to believe in God.

35 When it was daylight, the magistrates sent their officers to the jailer with the order: "Release those men." **36** The jailer told Paul, "The magistrates have ordered that you and Silas be released. Now you can leave. Go in peace."

37 But Paul said to the officers: "They beat us publicly without a trial, even though we are Roman citizens, and threw us into prison. And now do they want to get rid of us quietly? No! Let them come themselves and escort us out."

38 The officers reported this to the magistrates, and when they heard that Paul and Silas were Roman citizens, they were alarmed. **39** They came to appease them and escorted them from the prison, requesting them to leave the city. **40** After Paul and Silas came out of the prison, they went to Lydia's house, where they met with the brothers and encouraged them. Then they left.

Paul's love and concern
Philippians 1:7, 8, 27, 28; 2:2 page 10

7 It is right for me to feel this way about all of you, since I have you in my heart; for whether I am in chains or defending and confirming the gospel, all of you share in God's grace with me. **8** God can testify how I long for all of you with the affection of Christ Jesus.

27 Whatever happens, conduct yourselves in a manner worthy of the gospel of Christ. Then, whether I come and see you or only hear about you in my absence, I will know that you stand firm in one spirit, contending as one man for the faith of the gospel **28** without being frightened in any way by those who oppose you.

2 Make my joy complete by being like-minded, having the same love, being one in spirit and purpose.

In Thessalonica
Acts 17:1-9 page 11

1 When they had passed through Amphipolis and Apollonia, they came to Thessalonica, where there was a Jewish synagogue. **2** As his custom was, Paul went into the synagogue, and on three Sabbath days he reasoned with them from the Scriptures, **3** explaining and proving that the Christ had to suffer and rise from the dead. "This Jesus I am proclaiming to you is the Christ," he said. **4** Some of the Jews were persuaded and joined Paul and Silas, as did a large number of God-fearing Greeks and not a few prominent women.

5 But the Jews were jealous; so they rounded up some bad characters from the market-place, formed a mob and started a riot in the city. They rushed to Jason's house in search of Paul and Silas in order to bring them out to the crowd. **6** But when they did not find them, they dragged Jason and some other brothers before the city officials, shouting: "These men who have caused trouble all over the world have now come here, **7** and Jason has welcomed them into his house. They are all defying Caesar's decrees, saying that there is another king, one called Jesus." **8** When they heard this, the crowd and the city officials were thrown into turmoil. **9** Then they went bail for Jason and the others, and let them go.

Paul is worried
1 Thessalonians 2:17; 3:1-3 page 12

17 But, brothers, when we were torn away from you for a short time (in person, not in thought), out of our intense longing we made every effort to see you.

1 So when we could stand it no longer, we thought it best to be left by ourselves in Athens. **2** We sent Timothy, who is our brother and God's fellow-worker in spreading the gospel of Christ, to strengthen and encourage you in your faith, **3** so that no-one would be unsettled by these trials.

Paul's teaching in Athens
Acts 17:16-34 page 13

16 While Paul was waiting for them in Athens, he was greatly distressed to see that the city was full of idols. **17** So he reasoned in the synagogue with the Jews and the God-fearing Greeks, as well as in the market-place day by day with those who happened to be there. **18** A group of Epicurean and Stoic philosophers began to dispute with him. Some of them asked, "What is this babbler trying to say?" Others remarked, "He seems to be advocating foreign gods." They said this because Paul was preaching about Jesus and the resurrection. **19** Then they took him and brought him to a meeting of the Areopagus, where they said to him, "May we know what this new teaching is that you are presenting? **20** You are bringing some strange ideas to our ears, and we want to know what they mean." **21** (All the Athenians and the foreigners who lived there spent their time doing nothing but talking about and listening to the latest ideas.)

22 Paul then stood up in the meeting of the Areopagus and said: "Men of Athens! I see that in every way you are very religious. **23** For as I walked round and observed your objects of worship, I even found an altar with this inscription: TO AN UNKNOWN GOD. Now what you worship as something unknown I am going to proclaim to you.

24 "The God who made the world and everything in it is the Lord of heaven and earth and does not live in temples built by hands. **25** And he is not served by human hands, as if he needed anything, because he himself gives all men life and breath and everything else. **26** From one man he made every nation of men, that they should inhabit the whole earth; and he determined the times set for them and the exact places where they should live. **27** God did this so that men would seek him and perhaps reach out for him and find him, though he is not far from each one of us. **28** 'For in him we live and move and have our being.' As some of your own poets have said, 'We are his offspring.'

29 "Therefore since we are God's offspring, we should not think that the divine being is like gold or silver or stone—an image made by man's design and skill. **30** In the past God overlooked such ignorance, but now he commands all people everywhere to repent. **31** For he has set a day when he will judge the world with justice by the man he has appointed. He has given proof of this to all men by raising him from the dead."

32 When they heard about the resurrection of the dead, some of them sneered, but others said, "We want to hear you again on this subject." **33** At that, Paul left the council. **34** A few men became followers of Paul and believed. Among them was Dionysius, a member of the Areopagus, also a woman named Damaris, and a number of others.

In Corinth

Acts 18:1-11   page 17

1 After this, Paul left Athens and went to Corinth.

2 There he met a Jew named Aquila, a native of Pontus, who had recently come from Italy with his wife Priscilla, because Claudius had ordered all the Jews to leave Rome. Paul went to see them, **3** and because he was a tentmaker as they were, he stayed and worked with them. **4** Every Sabbath he reasoned in the synagogue, trying to persuade Jews and Greeks.

5 When Silas and Timothy came from Macedonia, Paul devoted himself exclusively to preaching, testifying to the Jews that Jesus was the Christ. **6** But when the Jews opposed Paul and became abusive, he shook out his clothes in protest and said to them, "Your blood be on your own heads! I am clear of my responsibility. From now on I will go to the Gentiles."

7 Then Paul left the synagogue and went next door to the house of Titius Justus, a worshipper of God. **8** Crispus, the synagogue ruler, and his entire household believed in the Lord; and many of the Corinthians who heard him believed and were baptized.

9 One night the Lord spoke to Paul in a vision: "Do not be afraid; keep on speaking, do not be silent. **10** For I am with you, and no-one is going to attack and harm you, because I have many people in this city." **11** So Paul stayed for a year and a half, teaching them the word of God.

Paul's letters to Macedonia

Philippians 2:22; 4:10, 11, 15   page 19

22 But you know that Timothy has proved himself, because as a son with his father he has served with me in the work of the gospel.

10 I rejoice greatly in the Lord that at last you have renewed your concern for me. Indeed, you have been concerned, but you had no opportunity to show it. **11** I am not saying this because I am in need, for I have learned to be content whatever the circumstances.

15 Moreover, as you Philippians know, in the early days of your acquaintance with the gospel, when I set out from Macedonia, not one church shared with me in respect to giving and receiving, except you only.

1 Thessalonians 3:6-9

6 But Timothy has just now come to us from you and has brought good news about your faith and

love. He has told us that you always have pleasant memories of us and that you long to see us, just as we also long to see you. **7** Therefore; brothers, in all our distress and persecution we were encouraged about you because of your faith. **8** For now we really live, since you are standing firm in the Lord. **9** How can we thank God enough for you in return for all the joy we have in the presence of our God because of you?

Teachings for the Thessalonians

1 Thessalonians 2:7-8; 4:3, 13-18; 5:16-19   page 20

7 As apostles of Christ we could have been a burden to you, but we were gentle among you, like a mother caring for her little children. **8** We loved you so much that we were delighted to share with you not only the gospel of God but our lives as well, because you had become so dear to us.

3 It is God's will that you should be holy.

13 Brothers, we do not want you to be ignorant about those who sleep, or to grieve like the rest of men, who have no hope. **14** We believe that Jesus died and rose again and so we believe that God will bring with Jesus those who sleep in him. **15** According to the Lord's own word, we tell you that we who are still alive, who are left till the coming of the Lord, will certainly not precede those who have fallen asleep. **16** For the Lord himself will come down from heaven, with a loud command, with the voice of the archangel and with the trumpet call of God, and the dead in Christ will rise first. **17** After that, we who are still alive and are left will be caught up with them in the clouds to meet the Lord in the air. And so we will be with the Lord for ever. **18** Therefore encourage each other with these words.

16 Be joyful always; **17** pray continually; **18** give thanks in all circumstances, for this is God's will for you in Christ Jesus. **19** Do not put out the Spirit's fire.

Instructions to the Corinthians

1 Corinthians 1:26-28; 14:26; 10:16, 17; 11:27, 28; 9:24, 25   pages 22-26

26 Brothers, think of what you were when you were called. Not many of you were wise by human standards; not many were influential; not many were of noble birth. **27** But God chose the foolish things of the world to shame the wise; God chose the weak things of the world to shame the strong. **28** He chose the lowly things of this world and the despised things—and the things that are not—to nullify the things that are.

26 What then shall we say, brothers? When you come together, everyone has a hymn, or a word of instruction, a revelation, a tongue, or an interpretation. All of these must be done for the strengthening of the church.

16 Is not the cup of thanksgiving for which we give thanks a participation in the blood of Christ? And is not the bread that we break a participation in the body of Christ? **17** Because there is one loaf, we, who are many, are one body, for we all partake of the one loaf.

27 Therefore, whoever eats the bread or drinks the cup of the Lord in an unworthy manner will be guilty of sinning against the body and blood of the Lord. 28 A man ought to examine himself before he eats of the bread and drinks of the cup.

24 Do you not know that in a race all the runners run, but only one gets the prize? Run in such a way as to get the prize. 25 Everyone who competes in the games goes into strict training. They do it to get a crown that will not last; but we do it to get a crown that will last for ever.

Paul leaves Corinth
Acts 18:18a, 19-23 page 27

18 Paul stayed on in Corinth for some time. Then he left the brothers and sailed for Syria, accompanied by Priscilla and Aquila. 19 They arrived at Ephesus, where Paul left Priscilla and Aquila. He himself went into the synagogue and reasoned with the Jews. 20 When they asked him to spend more time with them, he declined. 21 But as he left, he promised, "I will come back if it is God's will." Then he set sail from Ephesus. 22 When he landed at Caesarea, he went up and greeted the church and then went down to Antioch.

23 After spending some time in Antioch, Paul set out from there and travelled from place to place throughout the region of Galatia and Phrygia, strengthening all the disciples.

1 Corinthians 3:1-2; 16:15-16, 18

1 Brothers, I could not address you as spiritual but as worldly—mere infants in Christ. 2 I gave you milk, not solid food, for you were not yet ready for it. Indeed, you are still not ready.

15 You know that the household of Stephanas were the first converts in Achaia, and they have devoted themselves to the service of the saints. I urge you, brothers, 16 to submit to such as these and to everyone who joins in the work and labours at it. . . . 18 Such men deserve recognition.

Apollos
Acts 18:24-28 page 28

24 Meanwhile a Jew named Apollos, a native of Alexandria, came to Ephesus. He was a learned man, with a thorough knowledge of the Scriptures. 25 He had been instructed in the way of the Lord, and he spoke with great fervour and taught about Jesus accurately, though he knew only the baptism of John. 26 He began to speak boldly in the synagogue. When Priscilla and Aquila heard him, they invited him to their home and explained to him the way of God more adequately.

27 When Apollos wanted to go to Achaia, the brothers encouraged him and wrote to the disciples there to welcome him. On arriving, he was a great help to those who by grace had believed. 28 For he vigorously refuted the Jews in public debate, proving from the Scriptures that Jesus was the Christ.

Difficulties of Paul's life
2 Corinthians 11:23, 26-28; 1 Corinthians 9:16 page 29

23 Are they servants of Christ? (I am out of my mind to talk like this.) I am more. I have worked much harder, been in prison more frequently . . . .

26 I have been constantly on the move. I have been in danger from rivers, in danger from bandits, in danger from my own countrymen, in danger from Gentiles; in danger in the city, in danger in the country, in danger at sea; and in danger from false brothers. 27 I have laboured and toiled and have often gone without sleep; I have known hunger and thirst and have often gone without food; I have been cold and naked. 28 Besides everything else, I face daily the pressure of my concern for all the churches.

16 Yet when I preach the gospel, I cannot boast, for I am compelled to preach. Woe to me if I do not preach the gospel!

On baptism
Acts 19:1, 6, 7 page 30

1 While Apollos was at Corinth, Paul took the road through the interior and arrived at Ephesus. There he found some disciples.

6 When he placed his hands on them, the Holy Spirit came on them, and they spoke in tongues and prophesied. 7 There were about twelve men in all.

Romans 6:3-5, 11

3 Or don't you know that all of us who were baptized into Christ Jesus were baptized into his death? 4 We were therefore buried with him through baptism into death in order that, just as Christ was raised from the dead through the glory of the Father, we too may live a new life.

5 If we have been united with him in his death, we will certainly also be united with him in his resurrection.

11 In the same way, count yourselves dead to sin but alive to God in Christ Jesus.

Guidance for the Corinthians
1 Corinthians 5:1; 11:20-22; 14:22, 23, 29-31; 6:1; 1:12, 13 page 32

1 It is actually reported that there is sexual immorality among you, and of a kind that does not occur even among pagans: A man has his father's wife.

20 When you come together, it is not the Lord's Supper you eat, 21 for as you eat, each of you goes ahead without waiting for anybody else. One remains hungry, another gets drunk. 22 Don't you have homes to eat and drink in?

22 Tongues, then, are a sign, not for believers but for unbelievers; prophecy, however, is for believers, not for unbelievers. 23 So if the whole church comes together and everyone speaks in tongues, and some who do not understand or some unbelievers come in will they not say that you are out of your mind?

29 Two or three prophets should speak, and the others should weigh carefully what is said. **30** And if a revelation comes to someone who is sitting down, the first speaker should stop. **31** For you can all prophesy in turn so that everyone may be instructed and encouraged.

1 If any of you has a dispute with another, dare he take it before the ungodly for judgment instead of before the saints?

12 What I mean is this: One of you says, "I follow Paul"; another, "I follow Apollos"; another, "I follow Cephas"; still another, "I follow Christ."

13 Is Christ divided? Was Paul crucified for you? Were you baptized into the name of Paul?

Paul's prayer
2 Corinthians 2:4; 11:29 page 33

4 For I wrote you out of great distress and anguish of heart and with many tears, not to grieve you but to let you know the depth of my love for you. . . . **29** Who is weak, and I do not feel weak? Who is led into sin, and I do not inwardly burn?

1 Corinthians 1:4-9 page 34

4 I always thank God for you because of his grace given you in Christ Jesus. **5** For in him you have been enriched in every way—in all your speaking and in all your knowledge—**6** because our testimony about Christ was confirmed in you. **7** Therefore you do not lack any spiritual gift as you eagerly wait for our Lord Jesus Christ to be revealed. **8** He will keep you strong to the end, so that you will be blameless on the day of our Lord Jesus Christ. **9** God, who has called you into fellowship with his Son Jesus Christ our Lord, is faithful.

Philippians 1:21-24

21 For to me, to live is Christ and to die is gain. **22** If I am to go on living in the body, this will mean fruitful labour for me. Yet what shall I choose? I do not know! **23** I am torn between the two: I desire to depart and be with Christ, which is better by far; **24** but it is more necessary for you that I remain in the body.

Start of a letter
1 Corinthians 1:1-3 page 35

1 Paul, called to be an apostle of Christ Jesus by the will of God, and our brother Sosthenes,

2 To the church of God in Corinth, to those sanctified in Christ Jesus and called to be holy, together with all those everywhere who call on the name of our Lord Jesus Christ—their Lord and ours:

3 Grace and peace to you from God our Father and the Lord Jesus Christ.

Hymn to love
1 Corinthians 13:1-8 page 35

1 If I speak in the tongues of men and of angels, but have not love, I am only a resounding gong or a clanging cymbal. **2** If I have the gift of prophecy and can fathom all mysteries and all knowledge, and if I have a faith that can move mountains, but have not love, I am nothing. **3** If I give all I possess to the poor and surrender my body to the flames, but have not love, I gain nothing.

4 Love is patient, love is kind. It does not envy, it does not boast, it is not proud. **5** It is not rude, it is not self-seeking, it is not easily angered, it keeps no record of wrongs. **6** Love does not delight in evil but rejoices with the truth. **7** It always protects, always trusts, always hopes, always perseveres.

8 Love never fails.

You are sons, not slaves
Galatians 3:1, 26-28; 4:6-7; 5:14 page 36

1 You foolish Galatians! Who has bewitched you?

26 You are all sons of God through faith in Christ Jesus, **27** for all of you who were baptized into Christ have been clothed with Christ. **28** There is neither Jew nor Greek, slave nor free, male nor female, for you are all one in Christ Jesus.

6 Because you are sons, God sent the Spirit of his Son into our hearts, the Spirit who calls out, "*Abba*, Father." **7** So you are no longer a slave, but a son; and since you are a son, God has made you also an heir.

14 The entire law is summed up in a single command, "Love your neighbour as yourself."

The riot in Ephesus
Acts 19:23-30, 32, 35-41; 20:1-3 page 37

23 About that time there arose a great disturbance about the Way. **24** A silversmith named Demetrius, who made silver shrines of Artemis, brought in no little business for the craftsmen. **25** He called them together, along with the workmen in related trades, and said "Men, you know we receive a good income from this business. **26** And you see and hear how this fellow Paul has convinced and led astray large numbers of people here in Ephesus and in practically the whole province of Asia. He says that man-made gods are no gods at all. **27** There is danger not only that our trade will lose its good name, but also that the temple of the great goddess Artemis will be discredited, and the goddess herself, who is worshipped throughout the province of Asia and the world, will be robbed of her divine majesty."

28 When they heard this, they were furious and began shouting: "Great is Artemis of the Ephesians!" **29** Soon the whole city was in an uproar. The people seized Gaius and Aristarchus, Paul's travelling companions from Macedonia, and rushed as one man into the theatre. **30** Paul wanted to appear before the crowd, but the disciples would not let him. . . .

32 The assembly was in confusion: Some were shouting one thing, some another. Most of the people did not even know why they were there. . . .

35 The city clerk quietened the crowd and said: "Men of Ephesus, doesn't all the world know that the city of Ephesus is the guardian of the temple of the great Artemis and of her image, which fell from heaven? **36** Therefore, since these facts are undeniable, you ought to be quiet and not do anything rash. **37** You have brought these men here, though they have neither robbed temples nor blasphemed our goddess. **38** If, then, Demetrius and his fellow-craftsmen have a grievance against anybody, the courts are open and there are proconsuls. They can press charges. **39** If there is anything further you want to bring up, it must be settled in a legal assembly. **40** As it is, we are in danger of being charged with rioting because of today's events. In that case we would not be able to account for this commotion, since there is no reason for it." **41** After he had said this, he dismissed the assembly. . . .

1 When the uproar had ended, Paul sent for the disciples and, after encouraging them, said good-bye and set out for Macedonia. **2** He travelled through that area, speaking many words of encouragement to the people, and finally arrived in Greece, **3** where he stayed three months.

God loves a cheerful giver

2 Corinthians 7:4; 8:1-4, 7-9, 13; 9:7; 8:20　　　　page 39

4 I have great confidence in you; I take great pride in you. I am greatly encouraged.

1 And now, brothers, we want you to know about the grace that God has given the Macedonian churches. **2** Out of the most severe trial, their overflowing joy and their extreme poverty welled up in rich generosity. **3** For I testify that they gave as much as they were able, and even beyond their ability. Entirely on their own, **4** they urgently pleaded with us for the privilege of sharing in this service to the saints.

7 See that you also excel in this grace of giving.

8 I am not commanding you, but I want to test the sincerity of your love by comparing it with the earnestness of others. **9** For you know the grace of our Lord Jesus Christ, that though he was rich, yet for your sakes he became poor, so that you through his poverty might become rich.

13 Our desire is not that others might be relieved while you are hard pressed, but that there might be equality.

7 Each man should give what he has decided in his heart to give, not reluctantly or under compulsion, for God loves a cheerful giver.

20 We want to avoid any criticism of the way we administer this liberal gift.

Nothing can separate us from God

Romans 8:31-35, 37-39　　　　page 40

31 If God is for us, who can be against us? **32** He who did not spare his own Son, but gave him up for us all—how will he not also, along with him, graciously give us all things? **33** Who will bring any charge against those whom God has chosen? It is God who justifies. **34** Who is he that condemns? Christ Jesus, who died—more than that, who was raised to life—is at the right hand of God and is also interceding for us. **35** Who shall separate us from the love of Christ? Shall trouble or hardship or persecution or famine or nakedness or danger or sword? . . .

37 No, in all these things we are more than conquerors through him who loved us. **38** For I am convinced that neither death nor life, neither angels nor demons, neither the present nor the future, nor any powers, **39** neither height nor depth, nor anything else in all creation, will be able to separate us from the love of God that is in Christ Jesus our Lord.

Incident in Troas

Acts 20:7-12　　　　page 41

7 On the first day of the week we came together to break bread. Paul spoke to the people and, because he intended to leave the next day, kept on talking until midnight. **8** There were many lamps in the upstairs room where we were meeting. **9** Seated in a window was a young man named Eutychus, who was sinking into a deep sleep as Paul talked on and on. When he was sound asleep, he fell to the ground from the third storey and was picked up dead.

10 Paul went down, threw himself on the young man and put his arms around him. "Don't be alarmed," he said. "He's alive!" **11** Then he went upstairs again and broke bread and ate. After talking until daylight, he left. **12** The people took the young man home alive and were greatly comforted.

Farewell to the Ephesians

Acts 20:16-18, 22-25, 28-31, 32, 36-38　　　　page 42

16 Paul had decided to sail past Ephesus to avoid spending time in the province of Asia, for he was in a hurry to reach Jerusalem, if possible, by the day of Pentecost.

17 From Miletus, Paul sent to Ephesus for the elders of the church. **18** When they arrived, he said to them: "You know how I lived the whole time I was with you, from the first day I came into the province of Asia.

22 "And now, compelled by the Spirit, I am going to Jerusalem, not knowing what will happen to me there. **23** I only know that in every city the Holy Spirit warns me that prison and hardships are facing me. **24** However, I consider my life worth nothing to me, if only I may finish the race and complete the task the Lord Jesus has given me—the task of testifying the gospel of God's grace.

25 "Now I know that none of you among whom I have gone about preaching the kingdom will ever see me again. . . . **28** Guard yourselves and all the flock of which the Holy Spirit has made you overseers. Be shepherds of the church of God, which he bought with his own blood. **29** I know that after I leave, savage wolves will come in among you and will not spare the flock. **30** Even from your own number men will arise and distort the truth in order to draw away disciples after them. **31** So be on your guard! . . .

32 "Now I commit you to God and to the word of his grace, which can build you up and give you an inheritance among all those who are sanctified.

36 When he had said this, he knelt down with all of them and prayed. **37** They all wept as they embraced him and kissed him. **38** What grieved them most was his statement that they would never see his face again. Then they accompanied him to the ship.

PRINTED IN BELGIUM BY proost INTERNATIONAL BOOK PRODUCTION